It's Time to Rhyme . . .

The answer to every WORDY GURDY brain-teaser is a rhyming pair of words (like FAT CAT and DOUBLE TROUBLE) that will fit in the letter squares. The number after the definition tells you how many syllables are in each word.

. . . with **WORDY GURDY**®!

#10
WORDY GURDY®

by Ricky Kane

BERKLEY BOOKS, NEW YORK

WORDY GURDY #10

A Berkley Book / published by arrangement with
United Feature Syndicate, Inc.

PRINTING HISTORY
Berkley edition / November 1990

ISBN: 0-425-12433-9

A BERKLEY BOOK ® TM 757,375
Berkley Books are published by The Berkley Publishing Group,
200 Madison Avenue, New York, New York 10016.
The name "BERKLEY" and the "B" logo
are trademarks belonging to Berkley Publishing Corporation.

PRINTED IN THE UNITED STATES OF AMERICA

10 9 8 7 6 5 4 3 2 1

1. Call the cops (1)

☐☐☐☐☐■☐☐☐☐

2. Pseudo athlete (1)

☐☐☐☐■☐☐☐☐

3. Protected area for ferocious fish? (1)

☐☐☐☐☐☐■☐☐☐☐

4. Make up a purpose (2)

☐☐☐☐☐☐■☐☐☐☐☐☐

5. Col. North's exclamations? (2)

☐☐☐☐☐☐☐■☐☐☐☐☐☐☐

6. Some of Shoemaker's horses (2)

☐☐☐☐☐☐☐■☐☐☐☐☐☐☐

7. Data calculated to hurt someone (3)

☐☐☐☐☐☐☐☐☐■☐☐☐☐☐☐☐☐☐

2

1. 34th president's preferences (1)

☐☐☐☐☐■☐☐☐☐☐

2. Don't go, Sen. Goldwater (2)

☐☐☐☐☐■☐☐☐☐☐

3. Gerald flabbergasted (1)

☐☐☐☐☐■☐☐☐☐☐☐

4. Ron's spokesman's furtive glances? (1)

☐☐☐☐☐☐☐■☐☐☐☐

5. Indicate most important speech (2)

☐☐☐☐☐☐■☐☐☐☐☐☐

6. 31st president's hauling co. (2)

☐☐☐☐☐☐■☐☐☐☐☐☐

7. This is used to toast the winners & workers (2)

☐☐☐☐☐☐☐☐■☐☐☐☐☐☐☐☐

3

1. Leg of mutton (1)

☐☐☐☐■☐☐☐

2. Uncommon challenge (1)

☐☐☐☐☐☐☐☐

3. Cut clever remark from paper (1)

☐☐☐☐☐■☐☐☐☐

4. Dance of a tropical fruit (2)

☐☐☐☐☐☐■☐☐☐☐☐

5. Bareheaded mythological Titan (2)

☐☐☐☐☐☐☐☐☐☐☐☐

6. Thighbones of monkey's relative (2)

☐☐☐☐☐☐☐■☐☐☐☐☐☐

7. Pallette's pants (2)

☐☐☐☐☐☐☐☐☐☐■☐☐☐☐☐☐☐☐

4

1. Petite type of person (1)

☐☐☐☐☐☐■☐☐☐☐

2. Mrs. Nixon's low-heeled shoes (1)

☐☐☐☐■☐☐☐☐

3. Steal long-billed game bird (1)

☐☐☐☐☐■☐☐☐☐☐☐

4. Baby bringer's eating utensils (1)

☐☐☐☐☐☐■☐☐☐☐☐

5. Talkative rodent (2)

☐☐☐☐☐☐■■☐☐☐☐☐

6. Strange anxiety-ridden person (3)

☐☐☐☐☐☐■☐☐☐☐☐☐☐☐☐

7. Water pipes working fine (2)

☐☐☐☐☐☐☐☐■■☐☐☐☐☐☐☐

1. Final diet (1)

☐☐☐☐☐■☐☐☐☐

2. Traditional tales of long ago (1)

☐☐☐☐■☐☐☐☐

3. Unhappy Indian home (2)

☐☐☐☐☐■☐☐☐☐☐☐☐

4. Hat bought in Greek marketplace (3)

☐☐☐☐■☐☐☐☐☐

5. What Atlas did in playful mood? (1)

☐☐☐☐☐☐☐■☐☐☐☐☐

6. One who is afraid to look at himself (2)

☐☐☐☐☐☐■☐☐☐☐

7. Italian painter's expeditions (2)

☐☐☐☐☐☐☐☐■☐☐☐☐☐☐☐☐☐

1. Costello's trick (1)

☐☐☐☐ ■ ☐☐☐☐

2. Wildcat flirts (1)

☐☐☐☐ ■ ☐☐☐☐☐

3. Marshy area in Czech city (1)

☐☐☐☐☐☐ ■ ☐☐☐

4. Belly laugh (1)

☐☐☐☐☐ ■ ☐☐☐☐☐

5. Wood for building beds (2)

☐☐☐☐☐☐☐☐ ■ ☐☐☐☐☐☐

6. Certain breads for certain cats (2)

☐☐☐☐☐☐☐☐☐ ■ ☐☐☐☐

7. Attractive engraving (2)

☐☐☐☐☐☐☐☐ ■ ☐☐☐☐☐☐☐

7

1. Nursery school is one (1)

☐☐☐☐■☐☐☐☐

2. Meal made for state of mind (1)

☐☐☐☐☐■☐☐☐☐

3. Graffiti (1)

☐☐☐☐■☐☐☐☐☐

4. Rekindle longing (2)

☐☐☐☐☐☐■☐☐☐☐☐☐

5. Passes on trite remarks (2)

☐☐☐☐☐☐■☐☐☐☐☐☐☐

6. Muscular Indian (2)

☐☐☐☐☐☐■☐☐☐☐☐☐

7. Less-than-perfect private eye (3)

☐☐☐☐☐☐☐☐☐■☐☐☐☐☐☐☐☐☐☐☐

8

1. Sties and pens (1)

☐☐☐☐☐■☐☐☐☐

2. Sassy remark (1)

☐☐☐☐☐■☐☐☐☐

3. Indy 500 winner's car parts (1)

☐☐☐☐☐■☐☐☐☐☐

4. Saleslady's peculiarities (1)

☐☐☐☐☐☐■☐☐☐☐☐☐

5. Perfume only (2)

☐☐☐☐☐☐☐■☐☐☐☐☐

6. Bat man Rod's boats (2)

☐☐☐☐☐☐☐■☐☐☐☐☐☐

7. Austrian flowers (3)

☐☐☐☐☐☐☐☐☐■☐☐☐☐☐☐☐

11

1. Satiate William (1)

⬜⬜⬜⬜⬛⬜⬜⬜⬜

2. Sizzling journal (3)

⬜⬜⬜⬜⬜⬛⬜⬜⬜⬜⬜

3. Dillon's London digs (1)

⬜⬜⬜⬜⬜⬛⬜⬜⬜⬜⬜

4. One family's fights over meat (1)

⬜⬜⬜⬜⬜⬜⬜⬛⬜⬜⬜⬜⬜

5. Extension of hacienda (1)

⬜⬜⬜⬜⬜⬛⬜⬜⬜⬜⬜

6. Arlene foxtrots (2)

⬜⬜⬜⬜⬜⬜⬜⬛⬜⬜⬜⬜⬜

7. Type of heaven for voracious fish (3)

⬜⬜⬜⬜⬜⬜⬜⬜⬜⬛⬜⬜⬜⬜⬜⬜⬜⬜

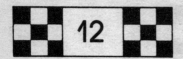

1. Droopy little devil (1)

☐☐☐☐☐■☐☐☐

2. What ones need scratching? (1)

☐☐☐☐☐☐■☐☐☐☐

3. D-day mission (1)

☐☐☐☐☐☐☐■☐☐☐☐☐

4. Trireme witticism (2)

☐☐☐☐☐☐☐■☐☐☐☐☐

5. Actor Williams' reservations (1)

☐☐☐☐☐☐☐☐■☐☐☐☐☐

6. No food for certain fish (2)

☐☐☐☐☐☐☐■☐☐☐☐☐☐☐

7. Funny man Don's barbs (2)

☐☐☐☐☐☐☐☐■☐☐☐☐☐☐☐☐☐

13

1. Japanese money changers (1)

☐☐☐■☐☐☐

2. Slammin' Sammy's necessities (1)

☐☐☐☐☐■☐☐☐☐

3. Mario's verse (2)

☐☐☐☐☐☐■☐☐☐☐☐

4. Sharply-dressed cartographer (2)

☐☐☐☐☐■☐☐☐☐☐

5. Exacting invention (2)

☐☐☐☐☐☐☐■☐☐☐☐☐

6. Coddles tent dwellers (2)

☐☐☐☐☐☐■☐☐☐☐☐☐

7. Famished while cutting roast (2)

☐☐☐☐☐☐☐☐☐■☐☐☐☐☐☐☐

1. Mopey Dick (1)

☐☐☐☐☐ ■ ☐☐☐☐☐

2. Whitewash squad (1)

☐☐☐☐☐ ■ ☐☐☐☐

3. Gainsay one's answer (2)

☐☐☐☐ ■ ☐☐☐☐☐

4. Disguise portable potable (1)

☐☐☐☐ ■ ☐☐☐☐☐

5. Authentic Caesar (2)

☐☐☐☐☐ ■ ☐☐☐☐☐☐

6. Revolutionary soprano (2)

☐☐☐☐☐ ■ ☐☐☐☐☐☐

7. Jackson's (of M.O.M.A.) larks (2)

☐☐☐☐☐☐☐☐☐☐ ■ ☐☐☐☐☐☐☐

15

1. Crypt (1)

| | | | | ■ | | | | |

2. Stopping place for tired tourists (1)

| | | | | | | | | |

3. Surmised the remainder (1)

| | | | | | | ■ | | | |

4. Come in, trusted counselor (2)

| | | | | | | | | |

5. License to be a recluse (2)

| | | | | | ■ | | | | | |

6. Simply annually (2)

| | | | | | ■ | | | | | |

7. Magazine piece about matter (3)

| | | | | | | | | ■ | | | | | | | |

1. Run, Sebastian! (1)

□□□□

2. Give Edna exam (1)

□□□□□■□□□□

3. Toss life preserver (1)

□□□□□■□□□□

4. Artificial flower (2)

□□□□□□□□■□□□□□□

5. Light wind, I beg you (1)

□□□□□□□■□□□□□□

6. Formally attired Loch monster (2)

□□□□□□□■□□□□□□

7. Ingenious stimulus (3)

□□□□□□□□□□□□■□□□□□□□□□□□

17

1. Burl's spouses (1)

| | | | | | ■ | | | | | |

2. Czech glutton (1)

| | | | | | | ■ | | | |

3. Joyce Carol's wraps (1)

| | | | | | ■ | | | | | |

4. Sir Walter's story lines (1)

| | | | | | ■ | | | | | |

5. One who hurries escort (2)

| | | | | | | | | | | | |

6. Forgot assignation (1)

| | | | | | | ■ | | | | |

7. Extremely difficult filling tank (3)

| | | | | | | | | ■ | | | | | | | |

18

1. Duck dinner (1)

☐☐☐☐☐■■☐☐☐☐

2. Flimsy legislation (1)

☐☐☐☐☐☐■☐☐☐☐

3. Irish Rose's husband, perhaps (2)

☐☐☐☐☐■☐☐☐☐☐☐

4. Friend to do homework with (2)

☐☐☐☐☐☐■☐☐☐☐☐

5. Journalist Jacob's articles (2)

☐☐☐☐☐■☐☐☐☐☐☐

6. Edna St. V.'s fish dinners (2)

☐☐☐☐☐☐☐■☐☐☐☐☐☐

7. These often pop at the dinner table (2)

☐☐☐☐☐☐☐☐■☐☐☐☐☐☐☐

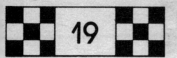

1. Convent race (1)

[ ][ ][ ][█][ ][ ][ ]

2. Pokes crustaceans (1)

[ ][ ][ ][ ][█][ ][ ][ ][ ][ ]

3. Exchanges fathers (1)

[ ][ ][ ][ ][ ][█][ ][ ][ ][ ]

4. Rug surface of cotton thread (1)

[ ][ ][ ][ ][ ][█][ ][ ][ ][ ]

5. Annelid's conditions (1)

[ ][ ][ ][ ][ ][█][ ][ ][ ][ ]

6. Sun tooth (2)

[ ][ ][ ][ ][ ][█][ ][ ][ ][ ]

7. Shelley's hairdressers? (2)

[ ][ ][ ][ ][ ][ ][ ][ ][█][ ][ ][ ][ ][ ][ ][ ][ ]

20

1. Fresh morning moisture (1)

□□□ ■ □□□

2. Octopus baby (1)

□□□□□ ■ □□□

3. Question influence (1)

□□□□□ ■ □□□□□

4. Jules' alloted times (1)

□□□□□□ ■ □□□□□

5. Awards jousters (1)

□□□□□□ ■ □□□□□□

6. Hate what one inherits (2)

□□□□□□□ ■ □□□□□□

7. Mythological Greek monster's aprons (3)

□□□□□□□□□□ ■ □□□□□□□□□□

21

1. Happy Turkish ruler (1)

2. Made a couple of bubbles (1)

3. High-masted sailing vessel (1)

4. Pulls wool over Verne's eyes (1)

5. Shute's demons (2)

6. Doing clerk's job happily (2)

7. Soothe Osmond & Dressler (2)

1. Information leak (1)

2. Fool parents (1)

3. Gritty cognac (2)

4. Calm leatherneck (2)

5. Plan a murder (2)

6. Fight over ironer (2)

7. Quiet occupant (3)

1. New potato growth (1)

☐☐☐☐■☐☐☐

2. Throw away good fortune (1)

☐☐☐☐☐■☐☐☐☐

3. Unchain Jupiter (1)

☐☐☐☐☐■☐☐☐☐

4. Oatmeal fight (2)

☐☐☐☐☐■☐☐☐☐

5. Medieval dog (2)

☐☐☐☐☐☐■☐☐☐☐☐

6. Believable food (3)

☐☐☐☐☐☐☐☐■☐☐☐☐☐☐

7. Dills for director Mike (2)

☐☐☐☐☐☐☐☐■☐☐☐☐☐☐☐

24

1. Refusal to take part in dialogue (1)

2. Huge social group (1)

3. Report from a loveboat (1)

4. Compliment receptacles used to carry food (1)

5. Kansas city? I have found it! (3)

6. Sad news (2)

7. Close look at rebellion at sea (3)

25

1. The KGB (1)

☐☐☐☐ ■ ☐☐☐☐

2. Certain provision in legislation (1)

☐☐☐☐ ■ ☐☐☐☐☐

3. More coquettish coquette (2)

☐☐☐☐☐ ☐☐☐☐☐

4. Unfamiliar mountains (1)

☐☐☐☐☐☐ ■ ☐☐☐☐☐

5. Make U.S. missile weigh less (2)

☐☐☐☐☐ ■ ☐☐☐☐

6. Slatted windows for 31st president (2)

☐☐☐☐☐☐ ☐☐☐☐☐☐

7. Grumbling while fixing toast (3)

☐☐☐☐☐☐☐☐☐☐ ■ ☐☐☐☐☐☐☐☐☐

26

1. Description of punk hairdo (1)

						■				

2. Young girl wandered from boundaries (1)

				■							

3. French goodbyes from baseball brothers (2)

					■						

4. Stylish government of Petain? (2)

					■					

5. Regrets felt by famous Chinese general (1)

						■					

6. Cheer and clap across the sea (2)

						■					

7. Dolt not given enough to eat (3)

								■										

27

1. Recorded music for monkeys? (1)

2. Times speed of object of hunt (1)

3. Depart from Allen or Martin (1)

4. "Chuck, meet Emmylou" (2)

5. Greeting from author Saul (2)

6. Iroquoian's nerve cells (2)

7. Needleworker's giggles (2)

28

1. Cereal enthusiast (1)

⬜⬜⬜⬜⬛⬜⬜⬜

2. Unusual challenge (1)

⬜⬜⬜⬜⬛⬜⬜⬜⬜

3. Be in debt, colloquially (1)

⬜⬜⬜⬛⬜⬜⬜⬜⬜

4. Crazy sealing compound (2)

⬜⬜⬜⬜⬛⬛⬜⬜⬜⬜

5. What Gregory uses to pay bills (1)

⬜⬜⬜⬜⬜⬛⬜⬜⬜⬜⬜

6. "Howard, meet the football commissioner" (2)

⬜⬜⬜⬜⬜⬜⬛⬜⬜⬜⬜⬜⬜

7. Made pledge to David of Old Testament (2)

⬜⬜⬜⬜⬜⬜⬜⬜⬜⬛⬜⬜⬜⬜⬜⬜⬜⬜

29

1. Makeup for brows and lashes (1)

| | | | ■ | | | |

2. Father's cutting tool (1)

| | | | | ■ | | | |

3. Try out a joke (1)

| | | | ■ | | | |

4. Select Jagger (1)

| | | | ■ | | | |

5. Joy, gratis (1)

| | | | ■ | | | |

6. Errol's cotton machines (1)

| | | | | | ■ | | | |

7. Merriment caused by speed (4)

| | | | | | | | | ■ | | | | | | | | |

1. Package smelting waste (1)

☐☐☐☐■☐☐☐☐

2. Bird's invited visitor (1)

☐☐☐☐■☐☐☐☐☐

3. Obeys Miranda law (1)

☐☐☐☐☐☐☐☐☐☐☐☐

4. Necklace for Oberon (1)

☐☐☐☐☐☐☐■☐☐☐☐☐☐

5. Fire whistles for English poet (2)

☐☐☐☐☐☐☐☐■☐☐☐☐☐☐☐

6. Rains warmed up (1)

☐☐☐☐☐☐■☐☐☐☐☐

7. Fuzzy fall of snow (2)

☐☐☐☐☐☐■☐☐☐☐☐☐

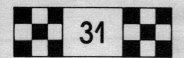

31

1. Area for telecommunications device (1)

2. Worries for Star of *Suspect* (1)

3. Guevara's words (1)

4. Bold little dried up fruit (2)

5. Comfort newsman Mike (2)

6. Carve small amount (2)

7. Making believe to be DA's opponent (3)

1. Inexpensive jalopy (1)

☐☐☐☐☐■☐☐☐☐

2. Big NCO (1)

☐☐☐☐☐■☐☐☐☐

3. Lightheaded L. Gordon of Watergate (2)

☐☐☐☐☐■☐☐☐☐

4. Gave urchin Oliver a smooch (1)

☐☐☐☐☐☐■☐☐☐☐

5. Fantastic state policeman (2)

☐☐☐☐☐■☐☐☐☐☐☐☐

6. Vehicles for Amadeus? (2)

☐☐☐☐☐☐☐☐☐■☐☐☐☐☐

7. Kitchen containers for runner Roger (3)

☐☐☐☐☐☐☐☐☐☐☐☐■☐☐☐☐☐☐☐☐☐

33

1. Meal with ambiance (1)

⬜⬜⬜⬜⬛⬛⬜⬜⬜⬜

2. Liberated actor Oliver (1)

⬜⬜⬜⬜⬜⬜⬜⬜⬜⬜

3. Patinkin on the beach (2)

⬜⬜⬜⬜⬜⬛⬜⬜⬜⬜⬜

4. Iacocca's beliefs (2)

⬜⬜⬜⬜⬜⬛⬜⬜⬜⬜⬜⬜

5. Thick soup made in humble home (2)

⬜⬜⬜⬜⬜⬜⬜⬛⬜⬜⬜⬜⬜⬜⬜

6. Newsman Dan's periods of agitation (2)

⬜⬜⬜⬜⬜⬜⬜⬛⬜⬜⬜⬜⬜⬜

7. Cures from newest supreme court justice (3)

⬜⬜⬜⬜⬜⬜⬜⬜⬜⬜⬛⬜⬜⬜⬜⬜⬜⬜⬜⬜

34

1. "Have a chew, pal?" (1)

⬜⬜⬜⬛⬜⬜⬜⬜

2. Medicine factory (1)

⬜⬜⬜⬜⬛⬜⬜⬜⬜

3. Actress Jessica's feelings of remorse (1)

⬜⬜⬜⬜⬜⬜⬛⬜⬜⬜⬜⬜

4. Salads for designer Geoffrey (1)

⬜⬜⬜⬜⬜⬛⬜⬜⬜⬜⬜⬜

5. "Let them eat cake" was one of these (2)

⬜⬜⬜⬜⬜⬜⬜⬜⬜⬛⬜⬜⬜⬜

6. Waiting on Berlin (2)

⬜⬜⬜⬜⬜⬜⬜⬛⬜⬜⬜⬜

7. Wax objects for actor Tony (2)

⬜⬜⬜⬜⬜⬜⬜⬜⬛⬜⬜⬜⬜⬜⬜⬜

35

1. Person Simple Simon met (1)
```
[ ][ ][ ][█][ ][ ][ ]
```

2. Shouts "wolf" several times (1)
```
[ ][ ][ ][ ][ ][█][ ][ ][ ][ ]
```

3. Managed to manage though sedated (1)
```
[ ][ ][ ][ ][ ][ ][█][ ][ ][ ][ ]
```

4. "Git along now, Mr. Grier." (2)
```
[ ][ ][ ][ ][ ][ ][ ][ ][ ][ ]
```

5. Men on Ahab's ship (2)
```
[ ][ ][ ][ ][ ][ ][ ][█][ ][ ][ ][ ][ ][ ][ ]
```

6. Attorneys for Twain's Tom (2)
```
[ ][ ][ ][ ][ ][ ][ ][ ][ ][ ][ ][ ][ ][ ][ ]
```

7. Palm stems from Philippine peninsula (2)
```
[ ][ ][ ][ ][ ][ ][ ][ ][ ][█][ ][ ][ ][ ][ ][ ][ ]
```

36

1. Description of mini mini skirt (1)

2. Small particles for Abner's pal (1)

3. Various aspects of labyrinth (2)

4. Wow Rathbone (2)

5. Concerns of oil rig fireman "Red" (2)

6. Thinner backstroker (2)

7. Feeling experienced by spurned lover (3)

1. Walking area (1)

2. Belgium (1)

3. Private eye's office (1)

4. Beauty salon (1)

5. Lady's purse in tough neighborhood (1)

6. Fresh water (1)

7. Orthodontist's office (1)

1. Melee on public conveyance (1)

☐☐☐☐■☐☐☐☐

2. Much ado about a kiss (1)

☐☐☐☐■☐☐☐☐☐

3. Drinks for French novelist Emile (2)

☐☐☐☐☐■☐☐☐☐☐

4. One who hires assassin (2)

☐☐☐☐☐☐■☐☐☐☐☐

5. British comic Hill's spinning machines (2)

☐☐☐☐☐☐■☐☐☐☐☐☐

6. Venerates gibbets (2)

☐☐☐☐☐☐☐■☐☐☐☐☐☐☐

7. A queen without a king is ... (2)

☐☐☐☐☐☐☐☐☐☐☐☐☐☐☐

39

1. Study harder (1)

☐☐☐☐☐■☐☐☐☐☐

2. "Another cup of tea, please." (1)

☐☐☐☐☐■☐☐☐☐☐

3. "Mr. Klein, meet Mr. Ailey." (2)

☐☐☐☐☐☐☐■☐☐☐☐☐☐

4. Save the grass (2)

☐☐☐☐☐☐■☐☐☐☐☐☐☐

5. Suddenly ailing (2)

☐☐☐☐☐☐☐☐■☐☐☐☐☐☐

6. Fonteyn's freight (2)

☐☐☐☐☐☐☐☐■☐☐☐☐☐☐☐

7. Levers for theatrical pub (2)

☐☐☐☐☐☐☐☐☐☐☐■☐☐☐☐☐☐☐☐☐

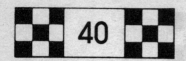

40

1. Long queue at Lourdes (1)

☐☐☐☐☐☐■☐☐☐☐☐

2. "Singer Horne, meet singer Easton." (2)

☐☐☐☐■☐☐☐☐☐☐

3. Comedian Benny's pratfalls (1)

☐☐☐☐☐■☐☐☐☐☐☐

4. Designer fashions for Milne donkey (2)

☐☐☐☐☐☐■☐☐☐☐☐

5. Gentle push (2)

☐☐☐☐☐☐■☐☐☐☐☐☐

6. Examines and verifies kudos (2)

☐☐☐☐☐■☐☐☐☐☐☐☐

7. Actor Leo's boyhood rocking toys (2)

☐☐☐☐☐☐☐■☐☐☐☐☐☐

41

1. Pit for fuel (1)

☐☐☐☐☐■☐☐☐☐

2. Game bird in the dell (1)

☐☐☐☐☐■☐☐☐☐

3. Risks going up flight of steps (1)

☐☐☐☐☐☐■☐☐☐☐☐☐

4. Risks being ogled (1)

☐☐☐☐☐☐■☐☐☐☐☐☐

5. Beg limited freedom from prison (2)

☐☐☐☐☐☐☐■☐☐☐☐☐

6. Darth's consumer advocates (2)

☐☐☐☐☐☐☐■☐☐☐☐☐☐☐

7. Area surrounded by water in former Siam (2)

☐☐☐☐☐☐☐☐☐■☐☐☐☐☐☐

42

1. Paid a penny (1)

2. Saw another pile of wood in bed (1)

3. Repair chimney (1)

4. Filch part of car (1)

5. Revolving disk of strong metal (1)

6. Poles for esnes (1)

7. Concealed refugees on right side of ship (2)

43

1. Breakfast food from Georgia (2)

2. Sigmund's blackouts? (1)

3. Put into law exactly as is (2)

4. Young girls who wear Bill's fashions (2)

5. Virile Kubrick (2)

6. Gold or silver type style in printing (3)

7. University student in Oslo (3)

44

1. In further pain (1)

□□□□□ ■ □□□□□

2. Glide upward again (1)

□□□□ ■ □□□□

3. Velvety part of face (1)

□□□□□ ■ □□□□

4. Rundown British truck (2)

□□□□□ ■ □□□□□

5. Arriving making throaty music (2)

□□□□□□ ■ □□□□□□

6. Lights for Shakespeare's theater? (1)

□□□□□□ ■ □□□□□□

7. Washing product making a comeback (3)

□□□□□□□□□ ■ □□□□□□□□□

45

1. Attractive couple (1)

☐☐☐☐☐■☐☐☐☐

2. So-so piece of fruit (1)

☐☐☐☐■☐☐☐☐

3. Hints from political party manager (1)

☐☐☐☐☐☐■☐☐☐☐

4. Nomad with a buzz on (2)

☐☐☐☐☐■☐☐☐☐☐

5. Unemployment compensation (2)

☐☐☐☐☐☐■☐☐☐☐☐☐

6. Hairdos for Ed Norton's wife (2)

☐☐☐☐☐☐☐■☐☐☐☐☐☐

7. Boatyard in Sicilian seaport (3)

☐☐☐☐☐☐☐☐■☐☐☐☐☐☐

1. "Make tracks, Mr. Spade." (1)

| | | | | | ■ | | | |

2. Comedian Arnold phoned (1)

| | | | | | | | |

3. Broader bill addendum (2)

| | | | | | | | | | |

4. Depression caused by drinking (1)

| | | | | | | | | |

5. Soldiers' basketball rims (1)

| | | | | | ■ | | | | | |

6. Stair parts for German emperor (2)

| | | | | | | | | | | | |

7. Scorn caused by car crash (3)

| | | | | | | | | | | | | ■ | | | | | | | | |

47

1. Another name for mint jelly (1)

2. Jazz session for young sheep (1)

3. Ohio senator's supporters (1)

4. Unfinished portrait by Renoir (1)

5. Consumer advocate's sorters (2)

6. Feeling sick while flunking (2)

7. Treacle for Jackie O (3)

1. Money paid to live in tepee (1)

2. Tear in fabric of camp shelter (1)

3. Disgrace arrived (1)

4. Meager bequest (1)

5. Recites lecture jottings (1)

6. "It's drizzling, Ms. Kazan." (2)

7. Fruit from Georgia (3)

49

1. Contort meaning (1)

☐☐☐☐☐☐☐■☐☐☐☐

2. Repair NY basketball team (1)

☐☐☐■☐☐☐☐☐☐

3. Slender waist cincher (1)

☐☐☐☐☐☐■☐☐☐☐

4. Fleshy flap dangled from mouth (1)

☐☐☐☐☐☐■☐☐☐

5. Actor Alan's dishes (1)

☐☐☐☐☐☐■☐☐☐☐

6. Animals for actress Cicely (2)

☐☐☐☐☐☐☐■☐☐☐☐☐☐

7. Ship yards for Mercouri (3)

☐☐☐☐☐☐☐☐■☐☐☐☐☐☐☐

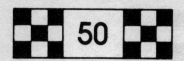

50

1. Annoy Mr. Rote (1)

☐☐☐☐ ■ ☐☐☐☐

2. Apportion grain (1)

☐☐☐☐ ■ ☐☐☐☐☐

3. Cuts down on thyme and dill (1)

☐☐☐☐☐ ■ ☐☐☐☐☐

4. Grouch's tricks (1)

☐☐☐☐☐☐ ■ ☐☐☐☐☐

5. Tease ghost (2)

☐☐☐☐☐ ■ ☐☐☐☐☐☐

6. Patriotic songs for small boxers (2)

☐☐☐☐☐☐☐ ■ ☐☐☐☐☐☐☐

7. Gabe's religious advisers (2)

☐☐☐☐☐☐☐☐ ■ ☐☐☐☐☐☐☐☐

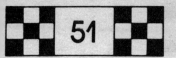

51

1. Golf scores for actor Jamie (1)

2. Despicable grin (1)

3. WW II correspondent Ernie's records (1)

4. Flighty old fussbudget (2)

5. Elude musical march (2)

6. Explain blueprint or drawing (2)

7. Tenon's partner for a turtle? (2)

52

1. Toy on a string that's only fair (2)

2. Fashions for amphibians (1)

3. Nasty tour conductor (1)

4. Calvin's collections (1)

5. Live-in vehicle for hiker (2)

6. Abolish affectionate touch (2)

7. Sauntering from casino to casino (2)

53

1. "Time to get up, Goldie." (1)

2. Provide shelter for cattle (1)

3. Bovine group for sewing machine man (1)

4. Surfer does this (1)

5. Swipes food from table (1)

6. Food for TV's Remington (1)

7. Lighting selected from various sources (3)

1. Get Philly Schmidt mentally prepared (1)

☐☐☐☐☐■☐☐☐☐

2. First aid kit (1)

☐☐☐☐■☐☐☐☐☐

3. Formerly class fool (1)

☐☐☐☐■☐☐☐☐

4. Constant whirlpool (2)

☐☐☐☐☐☐■☐☐☐☐

5. Sluggish flower (2)

☐☐☐☐☐☐■☐☐☐☐☐

6. Falling behind on supermarket job (2)

☐☐☐☐☐☐☐☐☐☐■☐☐☐☐☐☐

7. False show of goal guarding (2)

☐☐☐☐☐☐☐☐☐■☐☐☐☐☐☐☐☐

55

1. Tennis area on army base (1)

☐☐☐☐☐■☐☐☐☐☐

2. To whom do these wildebeests belong? (1)

☐☐☐☐☐■☐☐☐☐

3. Golf shots for Jeff's partner (1)

☐☐☐☐☐■☐☐☐☐☐

4. Counterfeit art of self defense (2)

☐☐☐☐☐☐■☐☐☐

5. Barkeep's binges (2)

☐☐☐☐☐☐☐■☐☐☐☐☐☐

6. N.J. Senator Bill, happily (2)

☐☐☐☐☐☐■☐☐☐☐☐☐

7. Apoplexy in Cairo (3)

☐☐☐☐☐☐☐☐■☐☐☐☐☐☐☐☐☐☐☐

56

1. Hesitation amazes (1)

☐☐☐☐☐☐■☐☐☐☐

2. Stared at newlywed (1)

☐☐☐☐☐■☐☐☐☐☐

3. Beds for friars (1)

☐☐☐☐☐☐■☐☐☐☐☐

4. Small body of water in Athens (1)

☐☐☐☐☐☐■☐☐☐☐☐

5. Prevent athletic contest (1)

☐☐☐☐☐☐☐☐☐☐☐

6. Gabor's Indian princes (2)

☐☐☐☐☐☐☐☐■☐☐☐☐☐

7. Drug dependency illness (3)

☐☐☐☐☐☐☐☐☐■☐☐☐☐☐☐☐☐☐☐

57

1. Sea plant (1)

2. Group of lions recoiled (1)

3. Stewed fruit for lunch (1)

4. Trims bushes at midday (1)

5. Hot alcoholic drink of inferior quality (2)

6. Musical instruments for Coretta (1)

7. Orthodontist in political middle (2)

58

1. Simply corrosion (1)

2. Vatican City's St. Peter's is a ... (1)

3. Meat sauce with ripples (2)

4. "Make amends, actress Dorothy." (2)

5. Gulps down capsules (1)

6. Meditation words for Mr. Claus (2)

7. Messengers for mink men (3)

59

1. Employ a trick (1)

2. Skinny relatives (1)

3. "Zebulon, meet DDE." (1)

4. Uptight fellows (1)

5. More despicable pursuer (2)

6. Young cow with less hearing (2)

7. Certain crisis for childbirth helper (2)

60

1. CB language (1)

2. Utensils for ex-supreme court nominee (1)

3. Imbibes one glass after the other (1)

4. Bowler does this, as does pitcher (1)

5. Repeat subject of forensic affair (2)

6. Floor refinishers for advice columnist (2)

7. Very funny water boy of the sky (4)

61

1. Put finish to a fad (1)

☐☐☐☐■☐☐☐☐☐

2. Fifth columnist's falsehoods (1)

☐☐☐☐■☐☐☐☐

3. Gloomy Indian (1)

☐☐☐☐☐■☐☐☐☐☐

4. Resting place for Navajo (1)

☐☐☐☐☐■☐☐☐☐☐

5. Hardships of living (1)

☐☐☐☐■☐☐☐☐

6. Overly nervous one taking potshots (2)

☐☐☐☐☐☐☐☐☐☐

7. Spanish cabin serving Italian dish? (3)

☐☐☐☐☐☐☐☐■☐☐☐☐☐☐☐

ANSWERS
1. END TREND 2. SPYS LIES 3. GRAVE BRAVE 4. BRAVE GRAVE
5. LIFE STRIFE 6. HYPER SNIPER 7. LASAGNA CABANA

1. Lion from Brazil (2)

2. Stay in the shade (1)

3. Half gainer rating low score (1)

4. Boleyn's supporters (1)

5. Excuse actress Eve (2)

6. Loud cold symptom letting up (2)

7. Demands from paying guests (2)

1. Light colored brew (1)

□□□□■□□□

2. Biscuits for actress Collins (1)

□□□□□□■□□□□□

3. Descendant's pride (2)

□□□□□□■□□□□□

4. Tricks soldiers (1)

□□□□□■□□□□

5. Don't feed Throneberry (1)

□□□□□□■□□□□

6. Skewered meat for Indian viceroy (2)

□□□□□□□■□□□□□□

7. Woman's prerogative (3)

□□□□□□□□■□□□□□□□□□

64

1. Yellowish-brown animal neck fur (1)

☐☐☐☐☐■☐☐☐☐☐

2. Eleventh president's gags (1)

☐☐☐☐☐☐■☐☐☐☐☐

3. More agile fabulist (2)

☐☐☐☐☐☐☐■☐☐☐☐☐

4. Recites from Joyce Carol's books (1)

☐☐☐☐☐☐☐☐■☐☐☐☐☐☐

5. More embarrassed hay spreader (2)

☐☐☐☐☐☐☐☐☐■☐☐☐☐☐

6. Bears witness to police seizures (2)

☐☐☐☐☐☐☐☐☐☐■☐☐☐☐☐☐☐

7. Spare time appropriation (2)

☐☐☐☐☐☐☐☐☐■☐☐☐☐☐☐☐

65

1. Selleck's senior dances (1)

☐☐☐☐☐■☐☐☐☐☐

2. Actress Myrna's savoir faire (1)

☐☐☐☐☐■☐☐☐☐☐

3. Pay Indian group for favor (1)

☐☐☐☐☐■☐☐☐☐☐☐

4. Door only for aristocrats (2)

☐☐☐☐☐☐■☐☐☐☐☐☐

5. Slogans for Preminger (2)

☐☐☐☐☐■☐☐☐☐☐

6. Reject sufficiently (2)

☐☐☐☐☐☐■☐☐☐☐☐☐☐

7. Discovering significance bit by bit (2)

☐☐☐☐☐☐☐☐☐■☐☐☐☐☐☐☐

1. Apple pastry lacking juice (1)

☐☐☐ ■ ☐☐☐

2. Large fruit (1)

☐☐☐ ■ ☐☐☐

3. Stylish Spartan (1)

☐☐☐☐ ■ ☐☐☐☐☐

4. Follows history of ethnic groups (2)

☐☐☐☐☐☐☐ ■ ☐☐☐☐☐

5. Liquid units for actor O'Toole (2)

☐☐☐☐☐☐ ■ ☐☐☐☐☐

6. "Potato bags, maybe?" (2)

☐☐☐☐☐☐ ■ ☐☐☐☐☐☐☐

7. Yuletide without spirit (2)

☐☐☐☐☐☐☐☐☐☐ ■ ☐☐☐☐☐☐☐☐☐☐

1. Grudge (1)

2. Refusal to continue verbal negotiations (1)

3. Not so much tension (1)

4. Budds buds (2)

5. Torment clergyman (2)

6. Visitor's searches (1)

7. Famous carom (2)

1. Wagon section (1)

☐☐☐☐☐■☐☐☐☐☐

2. Statue of deer on grass (1)

☐☐☐☐☐■☐☐☐☐☐

3. Hawaii or Alaska, chronologically (1)

☐☐☐☐☐■☐☐☐☐☐

4. Political platform went under (1)

☐☐☐☐☐■☐☐☐☐☐

5. Disgrace caused by athletic defeat (1)

☐☐☐☐☐■☐☐☐☐☐

6. Actor Boris in the distance (2)

☐☐☐☐☐☐☐■☐☐☐☐☐☐☐☐

7. Dense prickly bushes for bugs (2)

☐☐☐☐☐☐☐☐☐☐■☐☐☐☐☐☐☐☐☐

69

1. Mel's homers (1)

2. More serious hex (1)

3. Pointed cliff (1)

4. German river's grape crops (1)

5. Cabin where undies are made? (2)

6. Jim and Tammy's property (2)

7. Prospering behind the wheel (2)

70

1. Small piece of road atlas (1)

☐☐☐■☐☐☐☐☐

2. Burl's bee colonies (1)

☐☐☐☐■☐☐☐☐

3. Cuts down small wooded area (1)

☐☐☐☐☐■☐☐☐☐

4. Writes dates of secret dates (1)

☐☐☐☐☐☐■☐☐☐☐☐

5. Despising babbling (2)

☐☐☐☐☐☐■☐☐☐☐☐

6. Latest news from the north (2)

☐☐☐☐☐☐☐■☐☐☐☐☐

7. Farming savage (4)

☐☐☐☐☐☐☐☐☐■☐☐☐☐☐☐☐☐

71

1. Fewer clothes (1)

☐☐☐☐ ■ ☐☐☐☐☐

2. Poetic era (1)

☐☐☐☐☐ ■ ☐☐☐☐

3. Stories of college life in New Haven (1)

☐☐☐☐☐ ■ ☐☐☐☐☐

4. Applause from one's equals (1)

☐☐☐☐☐ ■ ☐☐☐☐☐

5. Flowers for the Say Hey kid (2)

☐☐☐☐☐☐☐ ■ ☐☐☐☐☐☐

6. Ghosts haunting one with personal liberty (2)

☐☐☐☐☐☐☐☐ ■ ☐☐☐☐☐

7. Pretending to be condescending (2)

☐☐☐☐☐☐☐☐☐ ■ ☐☐☐☐☐☐☐☐

1. Disease affecting certain flower (2)

2. Ships belonging to Greek island (1)

3. Headland with uneven surface (1)

4. Confronts orthodontia (2)

5. Slumber party in Mexico? (3)

6. Feel bitter about downfall (2)

7. Feelings expressed by slum residents (3)

73

1. Cautious Contrary Mistress (2)

2. Sheep-loser snoozing (2)

3. Dice rolls for nursery rhyme Mother (2)

4. Niche for Little Jack (2)

5. Toss spider-fearing girl around (2)

6. Find residence for Hansel's sister (2)

7. Wee Willie's fingers (2)

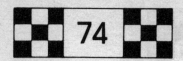

74

1. Clean certain type of statue (1)

☐☐☐☐☐☐■☐☐☐☐☐

2. Roman robe for Hindu discipline (2)

☐☐☐☐■☐☐☐☐

3. Rich cake made with wine (1)

☐☐☐☐☐■☐☐☐☐☐☐

4. "Paris air field, English actor Robert." (2)

☐☐☐☐■☐☐☐☐☐☐

5. Taller prickly plant (2)

☐☐☐☐☐☐■☐☐☐☐☐

6. British actor Michael's gray matter (1)

☐☐☐☐☐☐■☐☐☐☐☐☐☐

7. Giggles from roof timbers (2)

☐☐☐☐☐☐■☐☐☐☐☐☐☐☐

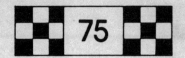

75

1. Ironic deep breath (1)

2. Sickle for cutting certain grain (1)

3. Gives wife a smooch (2)

4. Says "No" to boxed cake ingredients (2)

5. Widespread deceit (1)

6. Stephanie gives baleful glare (2)

7. Where Cole lived (2)

1. Veto legislative proposal (1)

☐☐☐☐☐■☐☐☐☐

2. Wound Lancaster's feelings (1)

☐☐☐☐☐☐☐☐

3. Despicable cunning (1)

☐☐☐☐☐☐☐☐☐

4. Complaint department phone (1)

☐☐☐☐☐■☐☐☐☐

5. Accomplishments of golfer Sam (1)

☐☐☐☐☐☐☐■☐☐☐☐

6. Shoes for singer Ella (2)

☐☐☐☐☐☐■☐☐☐☐☐☐

7. DDE, JFK, HHH, etc. (3)

☐☐☐☐☐☐☐☐☐☐☐☐■☐☐☐☐☐☐☐☐☐

1. One stealing pastry recipes? (1)

☐☐☐■☐☐☐

2. Mild snit (1)

☐☐☐☐■☐☐☐☐☐

3. Strange change in course (1)

☐☐☐☐☐■☐☐☐☐

4. Depression meal? (1)

☐☐☐☐☐■☐☐☐☐

5. Look up (1)

☐☐☐☐☐☐☐☐☐

6. Effect a brief cessation (1)

☐☐☐☐☐■☐☐☐☐

7. Friar's swim suit (1)

☐☐☐☐☐☐■☐☐☐☐☐

78

1. Entire strip of film (1)

2. Make legislation necessary (1)

3. Arrive at the coast (1)

4. Have enough money for trophy (2)

5. Squeezable actor Moore (2)

6. Keep chorus in a song or poem (2)

7. Watched parlor game pantomime (2)

79

1. Happy hockey star Park (1)

2. Statue of actress Collins? (1)

3. One picking up a sieve (2)

4. Accumulator's grocery list (2)

5. Actress Peggy's spectacles (2)

6. Drinking vessels for group of pupils (2)

7. Source of Texas clergyman's wealth? (2)

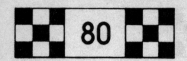

1. Siege of toe inflammation (1)

2. A wee bit constricting (1)

3. Soused arachnid (1)

4. Hamlet, at end of play (1)

5. Jalopy presenter (2)

6. Old Iranian translation (2)

7. Access to help for equine fish (2)

81

1. Insect-induced red welt on skin (1)

2. Is likely to take a nip (1)

3. Driller in more pain (2)

4. A shot for the heart (2)

5. More substantial basket material (2)

6. Putting a stop to warding off (2)

7. Lizard named for "The Great" (4)

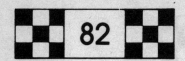

82

1. Place for Russian emperor to get a drink (1)

2. Fossilized skeleton part (1)

3. Be rude to group of students (1)

4. Money raised was awesome (1)

5. One who pesters homerun hitter (2)

6. Golf clubs for frontier mill owner (2)

7. Sorry about gambling again (3)

83

1. Non-violent contest (1)

☐☐☐☐☐■■☐☐☐☐

2. Puts jinx on both genders (2)

☐☐☐☐☐☐☐☐☐☐☐☐

3. Poolside slippers for giant ape (1)

☐☐☐☐☐☐■☐☐☐☐☐

4. Firmly imbeds spear (1)

☐☐☐☐☐☐☐☐■☐☐☐☐

5. Cut open house flora (1)

☐☐☐☐☐☐☐■☐☐☐☐☐

6. Preferences of *Ulysses* author (2)

☐☐☐☐☐☐☐☐☐☐☐☐☐☐☐

7. Bering Sea islands' answer to problem (3)

☐☐☐☐☐☐☐☐☐☐■☐☐☐☐☐☐☐☐☐

84

1. Marry the boss (1)

☐☐☐■☐☐☐☐

2. Not the first or second tofu, but the ... (1)

☐☐☐☐☐■☐☐☐☐

3. Use water pistol on coquette (1)

☐☐☐☐☐☐☐■☐☐☐☐☐

4. Lethal mixture (2)

☐☐☐☐☐☐■☐☐☐☐☐☐

5. Teeth of strikes-and-spares people (2)

☐☐☐☐☐☐☐■☐☐☐☐☐☐

6. Boss of apartment building entry guards (2)

☐☐☐☐☐☐☐☐■☐☐☐☐☐

7. Famous French bacteriologist's back-rubbers (2)

☐☐☐☐☐☐☐☐☐■☐☐☐☐☐☐☐☐☐

85

1. "The sun is rising, Mr. Connery." (1)

☐☐☐☐☐ ■ ☐☐☐☐☐

2. Is clothed in worries (1)

☐☐☐☐☐ ■ ☐☐☐☐☐

3. Pleasant sounding lamb sound (1)

☐☐☐☐☐☐ ■ ☐☐☐☐☐

4. Something causing thrills and chills (2)

☐☐☐☐☐☐☐ ■ ☐☐☐☐☐

5. Heavenly hosts (1)

☐☐☐☐☐☐ ■ ☐☐☐☐☐

6. Embarrassed young actress (2)

☐☐☐☐☐☐☐ ■ ☐☐☐☐☐☐☐

7. Race driver Mario's bits of colored paper (3)

☐☐☐☐☐☐☐☐ ■ ☐☐☐☐☐☐☐☐

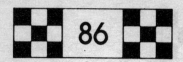

86

1. "Well, leave!" (1)

2. Dismiss Dad from company (1)

3. Dice player atop N. American continent (2)

4. Breaks thin shoulder bands (1)

5. Fasteners for thin shoulder bands (1)

6. Total shambles (2)

7. Wishing to regain one's job (3)

1. Polish hatchet (1)

2. Located a quid (1)

3. Bombard box for valuables from air (1)

4. Sigmund's vacuums (1)

5. One preaching doomsday at street junction (2)

6. Trips for a Ford (2)

7. Very slightly illegally (4)

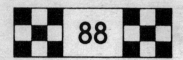

1. Sensible Wyman or Withers (1)

☐☐☐☐☐■☐☐☐☐☐

2. Pledges of Gordie or Elias (1)

☐☐☐☐☐■☐☐☐☐

3. Trace buildup of tooth coating (1)

☐☐☐☐☐■☐☐☐☐☐☐

4. Nudists, garmentwise (1)

☐☐☐☐☐☐☐■☐☐☐☐

5. Vegetables for former Molokai residents (2)

☐☐☐☐☐☐■☐☐☐☐☐☐

6. Turnip's kin in hightops eating tofu (2)

☐☐☐☐☐☐☐■☐☐☐☐☐☐

7. DJ who abhors phone calls is one who ... (2)

☐☐☐☐☐☐☐☐■☐☐☐☐☐☐☐

89

1. Cut transportation price (1)

2. Forbidden body decoration (2)

3. Buffaloes for heavyweight champ (2)

4. Average boredom (3)

5. Neck scarves for the Philly Phanatic (2)

6. Interior part of Scandinavian country (2)

7. Sparkling idea (2)

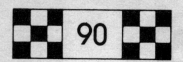

1. Spend money foolishly (1)

☐☐☐☐☐■☐☐☐☐☐

2. Ordered famous New England poet around (1)

☐☐☐☐☐☐■☐☐☐☐☐☐

3. Bowling alleys of Bangor (1)

☐☐☐☐☐☐☐☐☐☐

4. Takes a quick look, then screams (1)

☐☐☐☐☐■☐☐☐☐☐☐

5. Curdling calls of small Chinese dog (1)

☐☐☐☐☐■☐☐☐☐☐☐

6. Slatted blinds for 31st president (2)

☐☐☐☐☐☐☐☐■☐☐☐☐☐☐☐

7. Breathing spells for tyrants (2)

☐☐☐☐☐☐☐■☐☐☐☐☐☐☐

91

1. Famous chariot driver's mink coat (1)

☐☐☐☐☐☐☐☐

2. Comedian's boasts (1)

☐☐☐☐☐☐☐☐☐

3. Select animal parks (1)

☐☐☐☐☐☐☐☐☐☐

4. Characteristics of wife or husband (1)

☐☐☐☐☐☐☐☐☐☐☐

5. Certain organs of Flaubert's Emma (3)

☐☐☐☐☐☐☐☐☐☐☐☐☐☐

6. Famous fabulist's uppermost branches (2)

☐☐☐☐☐☐☐☐☐☐☐☐☐

7. Robe worn on a floating home (2)

☐☐☐☐☐☐☐☐☐☐☐☐☐☐☐☐☐☐☐☐

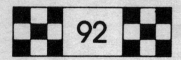

1. Three early autos of same make (2)

☐☐☐☐■☐☐☐☐

2. Licentious fellow (1)

☐☐☐☐■☐☐☐☐

3. "Son of Seth, meet goddess of love." (2)

☐☐☐☐■☐☐☐☐☐

4. Did not succeed, then turned ashen (1)

☐☐☐☐☐☐■☐☐☐☐☐☐

5. Earp's eating plans (2)

☐☐☐☐☐☐■☐☐☐☐☐

6. Lively jokester (2)

☐☐☐☐☐☐☐■☐☐☐☐☐☐☐

7. Condiments for long-legged game birds (2)

☐☐☐☐☐☐☐☐☐☐■☐☐☐☐☐☐☐☐

93

1. Negative responses from actor Aldo (1)

☐☐☐☐■☐☐☐☐

2. Fake martial art (2)

☐☐☐☐☐☐■☐☐☐☐

3. Extremely crafty (2)

☐☐☐☐☐☐■☐☐☐☐

4. What she does by the seashore (1)

☐☐☐☐☐■☐☐☐☐☐

5. Musts for politician "Boss" (1)

☐☐☐☐☐☐☐☐☐☐☐

6. Flowers for The Kid's bier (2)

☐☐☐☐☐☐■☐☐☐☐☐☐

7. Breakfast sweets for rowing crew (2)

☐☐☐☐☐☐☐☐☐■☐☐☐☐☐☐☐☐

1. Spread joy to Comet, Cupid, etc. (1)

☐☐☐☐☐■☐☐☐☐

2. Guide Rudolph *et al.* on proper course (1)

☐☐☐☐☐■☐☐☐☐

3. What Santa's vehicle does to presents (1)

☐☐☐☐☐■☐☐☐☐☐

4. Santa's journey in the dark (1)

☐☐☐☐☐■☐☐☐☐☐☐

5. Santa's vehicle off course? (1)

☐☐☐☐☐■☐☐☐☐☐☐

6. High class high spirits (like Santa's) (3)

☐☐☐☐☐☐☐■☐☐☐☐☐☐☐☐

7. Roof tops for Kris (2)

☐☐☐☐☐☐☐☐■☐☐☐☐☐☐☐☐☐

1. Tiny tinseled object (1)

☐☐☐■☐☐☐☐

2. Cold Christmas (1)

☐☐☐☐■☐☐☐☐

3. Cheery Christmas greenery (2)

☐☐☐☐☐■☐☐☐☐☐

4. Door decoration of waste land shrubbery (1)

☐☐☐☐☐■☐☐☐☐☐☐☐

5. Admire Yule log (1)

☐☐☐☐☐☐■☐☐☐☐☐

6. Creches for forest guardians (2)

☐☐☐☐☐☐☐■☐☐☐☐☐☐☐☐

7. Puffed up German Christmas bread (2)

☐☐☐☐☐☐■☐☐☐☐☐☐☐

1. Bargain prices on face nets (1)

☐☐☐☐ ■ ☐☐☐☐

2. Indians' scriptures (2)

☐☐☐☐☐☐ ■ ☐☐☐☐☐

3. Writer Gertrude's drinks (1)

☐☐☐☐☐☐ ■ ☐☐☐☐☐

4. Writer Gertrude's complaints (1)

☐☐☐☐☐☐ ■ ☐☐☐☐☐☐

5. More embarrassed pot mender (2)

☐☐☐☐☐☐ ■ ☐☐☐☐☐☐

6. Castle cup (2)

☐☐☐☐☐☐ ■ ☐☐☐☐☐☐☐

7. Comedian Joan has the chills (2)

☐☐☐☐☐☐ ■ ☐☐☐☐☐☐☐

1. Be well acquainted with Ziegfeld (1)

☐☐☐☐☐■☐☐☐

2. Painfully uncomfortable sofa (1)

☐☐☐☐☐■☐☐☐☐

3. Motionless humorist Rogers (1)

☐☐☐☐☐■■☐☐☐☐

4. Leave distillery to heirs (1)

☐☐☐☐☐■☐☐☐☐

5. Golfer Palmer's fans (2)

☐☐☐☐☐☐■☐☐☐☐☐

6. Impede actress Veronica (2)

☐☐☐☐☐☐☐■☐☐☐☐

7. Safari wear for Onassis (2)

☐☐☐☐☐☐☐■☐☐☐☐☐

98

1. Where to take a bath underwater (1)

2. Peas' police department? (1)

3. Contradict Whitney or Wallach (2)

4. Therefore, the sixth sign of the zodiac (2)

5. Improved secretarial effort (2)

6. More intelligent author of *Sister Carrie* (2)

7. Less interesting Henley participant (2)

99

1. Modest target of swatter (1)

⬜⬜⬜⬛⬜⬜⬜

2. Manufactured knife part (1)

⬜⬜⬜⬜⬜⬛⬜⬜⬜⬜

3. Most minimally cheated (1)

⬜⬜⬜⬜⬜⬜⬛⬜⬜⬜⬜⬜⬜⬜

4. Laud a meaningful group of words (1)

⬜⬜⬜⬜⬜⬜⬜⬜⬜⬜⬜⬜⬜

5. Odd Couple's Felix, many years ago (2)

⬜⬜⬜⬜⬜⬜⬛⬜⬜⬜⬜⬜⬜

6. Skinny seamstress (2)

⬜⬜⬜⬜⬜⬜⬛⬜⬜⬜⬜⬜⬜

7. Elizabeth Barrett's fiance fooling around (2)

⬜⬜⬜⬜⬜⬜⬜⬛⬜⬜⬜⬜⬜⬜⬜⬜

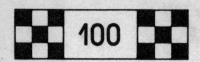

1. The evils of martinis etc. (1)

2. Approach keg with caution (1)

3. Falana's sensible New Year's Eve drinks (2)

4. Reach destination safely with sober driver (2)

5. One who stays sober at New Year's affair (2)

6. Dangerous scotch, rye, etc. (2)

7. Intelligent imbibing (2)

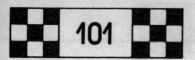

1. QB gives go-ahead to pass catchers (1)

⬜⬜⬜⬜⬜⬜⬛⬜⬜⬜⬜⬜

2. Challenges Chicago football team (1)

⬜⬜⬜⬜⬜⬜⬛⬜⬜⬜⬜⬜

3. After Lombardi (1)

⬜⬜⬜⬜⬜⬛⬜⬜⬜⬜⬜

4. Limber New York football player (2)

⬜⬜⬜⬜⬜⬜⬜⬜⬛⬜⬜⬜⬜⬜

5. One who tackles Green Bay QB (2)

⬜⬜⬜⬜⬜⬜⬛⬜⬜⬜⬜⬜⬜

6. Minnesota football team's preferences (2)

⬜⬜⬜⬜⬜⬜⬜⬛⬜⬜⬜⬜⬜⬜⬜

7. Watched Rose Bowl preceder (2)

⬜⬜⬜⬜⬜⬜⬜⬜⬛⬜⬜⬜⬜⬜⬜

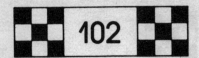

102

1. Sleepwear for radio music man (2)

□□□□ ■ □□□

2. Grange ran away (1)

□□□□ ■ □□□□

3. Drastic telegram (1)

□□□□□□ ■ □□□□

4. Wind direction indicator in Bar Harbor (1)

□□□□□□□ ■ □□□□□

5. "Nonsense, Mr. Jourdan." (2)

□□□□□□□□ ■ □□□□

6. Extremely serious author Jules (1)

□□□□□ ■ □□□□□

7. Marble excavation under twinkling sky (2)

□□□□□□□□ ■ □□□□□□

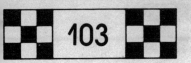

103

1. Hunger strike over (1)

2. Plagiarizing author (1)

3. Grew noticeably older in jail (1)

4. Overtook at great speed (1)

5. Fold rental agreement (1)

6. Meat for actress Sylvia (2)

7. Squirming while giving 10% to church (2)

104

1. Dunce hat (1)

2. "Certainly, Mrs. Hussein." (1)

3. Firestarters for actor with 7-year-itch (2)

4. Drums from certain part of Africa (2)

5. Long-snouted mammals' frolics (2)

6. Those dunning Ann or Mitch (2)

7. Kimonos for '20s girls (2)

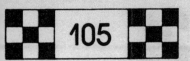

1. Cafeteria item temporarily missing (1)

☐☐☐☐☐☐■☐☐☐

2. "Little" comic strip girl's Eskimo knives (2)

☐☐☐☐☐☐☐☐☐

3. Amusing rhyme (2)

☐☐☐☐☐■☐☐☐☐☐

4. Put off tooth deterioration (2)

☐☐☐☐☐■☐☐☐☐☐

5. Cheerful acting foolish (2)

☐☐☐☐☐■☐☐☐☐☐

6. Flour refiners for funny Phyllis (2)

☐☐☐☐☐☐☐■☐☐☐☐☐☐

7. Early Peruvians for Honest Abe (2)

☐☐☐☐☐☐☐☐☐■☐☐☐☐☐☐

1. Already left (1)

| | | | | ■ | | | |

2. Ump makes certain decisions (1)

| | | | | | ■ | | | | | |

3. Less crazy window glass replacer (2)

| | | | | | ■ | | | | | |

4. Dying in debt (2)

| | | | | | ■ | | | | |

5. Dislikes braids (1)

| | | | | | ■ | | | | |

6. Less recent circular (2)

| | | | | | ■ | | | | | |

7. Henri's daughter's marriage linens, etc. (2)

| | | | | | | | | ■ | | | | | | | | |

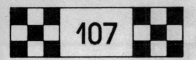

1. Sounds of wild swine (1)

2. Taking out a boat with oars (2)

3. Promise irresistibility (2)

4. One clink of coins or spurs (2)

5. One watching type of pool game (2)

6. Juggle skills (2)

7. Painted with dots though handicapped (2)

1. Funereal flame (1)

☐☐☐☐☐ ☐☐☐☐

2. Coffee cups for hoods? (1)

☐☐☐☐☐ ☐☐☐☐

3. Jostle fall guy (1)

☐☐☐☐ ☐☐☐☐☐

4. One putting an end to gossip (2)

☐☐☐☐☐☐☐☐☐☐

5. Knife for bread spread (2)

☐☐☐☐☐☐ ☐☐☐☐☐☐

6. Happy honeybunch (2)

☐☐☐☐☐ ☐☐☐☐☐☐

7. One who sorts baby teethers (4)

☐☐☐☐☐☐☐☐☐ ☐☐☐☐☐☐☐☐☐☐

109

1. Harbinger from Italy (2)

2. Sounds from reddish-brown horse (1)

3. Not suitable without light (2)

4. Hair lighteners for hermits (2)

5. One making louvered window cover (2)

6. Blooming section of lower NY city (3)

7. Furniture for World War I infantryman (2)

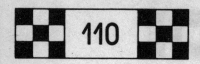

110

1. British crown colony in China (1)

☐☐☐☐■☐☐☐☐

2. Cotton fabric from Peru (2)

☐☐☐☐☐☐☐☐

3. "Twist and turn, Mr. Stewart." (2)

☐☐☐☐☐☐■☐■☐☐☐

4. One small rush of excitement (2)

☐☐☐☐☐☐■☐☐☐☐☐

5. Engine parts for prizefighter Sonny (2)

☐☐☐☐☐☐■☐☐☐☐☐☐

6. Satire of cooking contest (2)

☐☐☐☐☐■☐☐☐☐☐☐

7. Smokin' Joe's smokin' coal containers (2)

☐☐☐☐☐☐☐■☐☐☐☐☐☐

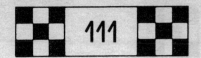

1. Fowl on French Riviera (1)

☐☐☐☐☐ ☐☐☐☐☐☐

2. Herb of highest quality (1)

☐☐☐☐☐ ☐☐☐☐☐

3. Renowned passage of water (1)

☐☐☐☐☐ ☐☐☐☐☐☐

4. Pester homerun king Roger (2)

☐☐☐☐☐☐ ☐☐☐☐☐

5. Hobo's temporary homes (1)

☐☐☐☐☐ ☐☐☐☐☐

6. Bread from the oven (1)

☐☐☐☐☐☐ ☐☐☐☐☐☐

7. Publishers of Shelley's book (2)

☐☐☐☐☐☐☐ ☐☐☐☐☐☐☐☐

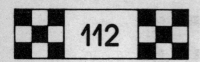

112

1. Undressed food (1)

2. Fulton fantasy that came true (1)

3. "That's the hunter in the sky, Hugh." (3)

4. Impair man of the cloth (2)

5. Pieces of pie for TV PI (2)

6. Massachusetts descendants of author Jane (2)

7. Kicking football with noisy effort (2)

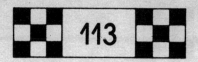

113

1. Shoshonean's shoes (1)

2. Sloppy form (2)

3. Braids for Shakespeare's shrew (1)

4. Agreement full of substance (2)

5. Dark reddish-brown wood (2)

6. Exclusive place of seclusion (2)

7. Instruction amendment (3)

1. Cable car for baby carriages? (1)

☐☐☐☐☐■☐☐☐☐

2. Place to store tots' wooden cubes (1)

☐☐☐☐☐☐☐☐☐☐

3. Theater area for bandleader Ray (1)

☐☐☐☐☐☐☐☐☐☐

4. More ticked-off totaler (2)

☐☐☐☐☐■☐☐☐☐☐

5. Unfamiliar mountains (1)

☐☐☐☐☐☐■☐☐☐☐

6. Nocturnal Nazi sound (2)

☐☐☐☐☐☐☐☐■☐☐☐☐☐☐

7. Washing procedures of certain Eskimos (3)

☐☐☐☐☐☐☐☐☐☐☐☐■☐☐☐☐☐☐☐☐☐☐

1. Used to be a policeman (1)

☐☐☐■☐☐☐☐

2. Author Philip's arboreal mammals (1)

☐☐☐☐☐■☐☐☐☐☐

3. Big cats for author Thomas (2)

☐☐☐☐☐☐■☐☐☐☐☐

4. Didn't get charred (1)

☐☐☐☐☐☐■☐☐☐☐☐

5. Miss Dunne's polymers (2)

☐☐☐☐☐☐☐■☐☐☐☐☐☐☐

6. Cause of tooth coating (2)

☐☐☐☐☐☐■☐☐☐☐☐☐

7. Scorn from Australian seaport (2)

☐☐☐☐☐☐☐☐☐■☐☐☐☐☐☐

116

1. Sedaka's business agreements (1)

| | | | | | | | ■ | | | | | | | |

2. Kingdoms of threatened trees (1)

| | | | ■ | | | | | |

3. Late British actor David obsessed? (2)

| | | | | | ■ | | | | | | | |

4. Wimpy whippoorwill (2)

| | | | | | | ■ | | | | | |

5. Bagging coarse woven material (2)

| | | | | | | ■ | | | | | | | |

6. Being victorious in wrestling match (2)

| | | | | | | ■ | | | | | | |

7. History of ups and downs (2)

| | | | | | | | ■ | | | | | | |

117

1. One who bought a ticket but didn't use it (1)

□□■□□□□

2. Males' desires (1)

□□□□□□□□

3. Control post of dominion (1)

□□□□□□■□□□□

4. Bossies nod off (1)

□□□□□□□□□□

5. Workers' co-ops in Clint's town? (2)

□□□□□□□■□□□□

6. Brightly-colored upright water pipe (2)

□□□□□□□□■□□□□□□□

7. Angels hovering over lawman (2)

□□□□□□□□□■□□□□□□□□

118

1. Chilled container for gelatin salad (1)

☐☐☐☐☐☐☐☐☐☐

2. One in charge of cream, hard or hot fudge (1)

☐☐☐☐☐☐☐☐☐☐☐

3. Clean vegetable (1)

☐☐☐☐☐☐☐☐☐☐☐

4. Add yeast to a baker's half-dozen + 1 (2)

☐☐☐☐☐☐☐☐☐☐☐☐☐

5. Dad's potato-based liquor (1)

☐☐☐☐☐☐☐☐☐☐☐☐

6. Fearful of annual march (2)

☐☐☐☐☐☐☐☐☐☐☐☐

7. Prayer at deer hunter's table (3)

☐☐☐☐☐☐☐☐☐☐☐☐☐☐☐☐☐

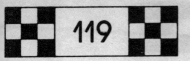

1. Vessel patrolling castle (1)

☐☐☐☐☐ ■ ☐☐☐☐

2. Comedian's luggage (1)

☐☐☐☐ ☐☐☐☐

3. Careless hyphen (1)

☐☐☐☐ ☐☐☐☐

4. More depressed audible critic (2)

☐☐☐☐☐☐ ■ ☐☐☐☐☐

5. Fresh water ducks for Norman Vincent (1)

☐☐☐☐☐☐ ■ ☐☐☐☐☐

6. IOUs (2)

☐☐☐☐☐☐☐☐ ■ ☐☐☐☐☐☐☐

7. Make war again against Washington port (3)

☐☐☐☐☐☐☐☐☐☐ ■ ☐☐☐☐☐☐☐

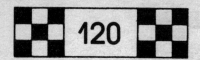

120

1. Where Fort Knox bars come from (1)

2. Greases springs (1)

3. Hit upon good fortune (1)

4. Hairdo for baby Milton? (1)

5. Sly looks from Cyrus (2)

6. Sun orbiter made of feldspar and quartz? (2)

7. Law-breaking Monk of musical fame? (4)

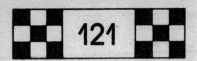

121

1. Annoy Christopher (1)

☐☐☐☐☐☐■☐☐☐☐☐☐

2. Elaine's Eskimo craft (2)

☐☐☐☐☐☐☐☐☐☐☐☐

3. Wm. Randolph's franks (1)

☐☐☐☐☐☐☐☐■☐☐☐☐☐☐☐☐

4. DeWitt's decisions (2)

☐☐☐☐☐■☐☐☐☐☐☐☐☐☐

5. Roberta's glasses (2)

☐☐☐☐☐■☐☐☐☐☐☐☐☐☐☐

6. Monica's space trips (2)

☐☐☐☐☐☐☐☐■☐☐☐☐☐☐☐

7. Geoffrey's cup holders (2)

☐☐☐☐☐☐☐☐☐■☐☐☐☐☐☐☐

1. Road named for Marion Morrison (1)

[ ][ ][ ][ ][ ][ ][█][ ][ ][ ][ ][ ]

2. Lounge of Doris van Kappelhoff (1)

[ ][ ][ ][ ][ ][█][ ][ ][ ][ ][ ][ ]

3. Breads made by Margarita Cansino (2)

[ ][ ][ ][ ][ ][ ][ ][ ][ ][ ][ ][ ]

4. Unsteady Rose Louise Hovick (2)

[ ][ ][ ][ ][ ][█][ ][ ][ ][ ][ ][ ]

5. Gems belonging to Lucille Le Sueur (1)

[ ][ ][ ][ ][ ][ ][█][ ][ ][ ][ ][ ]

6. Horses owned by Bernard Schwartz (2)

[ ][ ][ ][ ][ ][ ][█][ ][ ][ ][ ][ ]

7. Sweets made by Allen Konigsberg (2)

[ ][ ][ ][ ][ ][ ][ ][█][ ][ ][ ][ ][ ]